William M. Gaines's

DR. JEKYLL & MR. MAD

Edited by Albert B. Feldstein

WARNER BOOKS

A Warner Communications Company

Victims of "Cliche Conversation" . . .
unite! You have nothing to lose but
your utter boredom! Yes, here's your
chance to strike back! Unfortunately,
you will probably end up with nobody
talking to you once you start using:

ARTIST: GEORGE WOODBRIDGE   WRITER: STAN HART

MAD'S
"CLICHE CONVERSATION" KILLERS

AT A REUNION PARTY

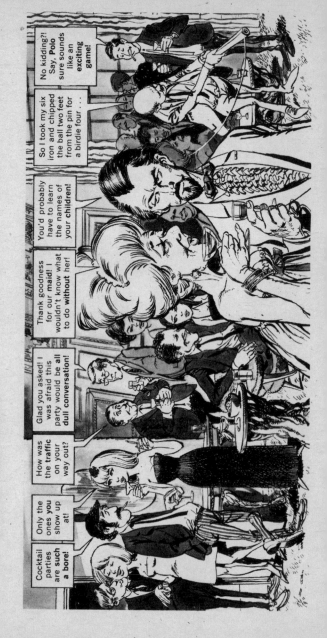

IN A DOCTOR'S OFFICE

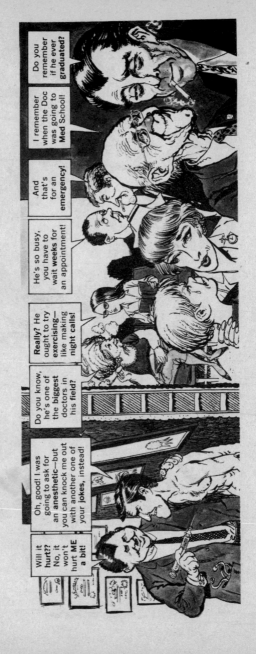

AT A SURPRISE PARTY

IN AN ART MUSEUM

ONE
DAY
IN AN
OFFICE

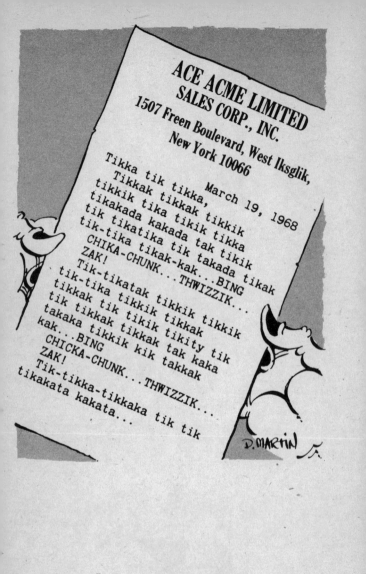

HITTING BELOW THE BLACK BELT DEPT.

TODAY, MORE THAN EVER BEFORE, PEOPLE ARE INTERESTED IN LEARNING
TO DEFEND THEMSELVES. IF YOU'RE LIKE THE REST OF US, YOU PROBABLY
HAVE SOME BIG LUG WHO'S ALWAYS BULLYING YOU. WELL, ISN'T IT TIME
YOU STOOD UP TO YOUR WIFE? THERE ARE DOZENS OF BOOKS ON THE MARKET
DEALING WITH SELF-DEFENSE. MANY OF THEM ARE EVEN BROKEN DOWN INTO
CATEGORIES, SUCH AS "SELF-DEFENSE FOR MEN" "SELF-DEFENSE FOR
WOMEN", "SELF-DEFENSE FOR BOYS", AND SO ON. WELL, MAD WOULD LIKE
TO ADD TO THIS RIDICULOUS COLLECTION OF "SELF-DEFENSE BOOKS" WITH

MORE

SPECIALIZED

SELF-DEFENSE

BOOKS

ARTIST: JOE ORLANDO

WRITER: DICK DE BARTOLO

SELF-DEFENSE FOR LITTLE OLD LADIES

HOW TO WHIP THAT YOUNG WHIPPERSNAPPER

●

Seven Defense Devices You Can Hide In Your Orthopedic Shoes

●

HOW TO KNIT A 20-POUND CHAIN INTO YOUR SHAWL

●

A Concealed Hat Pin: Your Most Cherished Defense Weapon

●

HOW TO BITE A MUGGER WITHOUT LEAVING YOUR FALSE TEETH IN HIS ARM

●

Build Your Own Bullet-Proof Corset

●

18 TERRIBLE THINGS YOU CAN DO WITH AN UMBRELLA

Self-Defense For
POLICEMEN

★ ★ ★

**12 WAYS TO STOP A CRIMINAL
WITH JUST ONE FINGER**
(Your Trigger Finger)

★ ★ ★

**HOW TO DEFEND YOURSELF
AGAINST ONE ATTACKER**

★ ★ ★

How To Defend Yourself
Against One Attacker With
A Crowd Of 500 Watching

★ ★ ★

**HOW TO DEFEND YOURSELF
AGAINST 501 ATTACKERS**

★ ★ ★

The Only Sure Way To Avoid
A Riot: GO OFF DUTY!

★ ★ ★

**18 WAYS TO DEFEND
YOURSELF AGAINST
AN IRATE LITTLE OLD
LADY WITH AN UMBRELLA**

★ ★ ★

Self-Defense For
TEENY-BOPPERS

IF A THUG GRABS FOR YOUR PURSE...LET HIM HAVE IT!
(He Deserves The Hernia)

□ □ □ □

How To Defend Yourself Against Your Boyfriend ... Or An Octopus

□ □ □ □

TEN THINGS TO SAY TO FRESH GUYS WHO WHISTLE AT YOU

□ □ □ □

15 Streets Where You Can Find Fresh Guys To Whistle At You

□ □ □ □

GET THE EFFECT OF BRASS KNUCKLES WITH 4 FRIENDSHIP RINGS

□ □ □ □

How To Hide A Mini-Knife Under Your Mini-Skirt

□ □ □ □

THE BEST DEFENSE: RUN FASTER THAN YOUR NYLONS

Self-Defense For
TINY TOTS

IT'S YOUR ICE CREAM—DEFEND IT!
A Collection Of Punches & Blocks
That Only Use Your Free Hand

* * *

CONVERT YOUR CAP PISTOL
INTO THE REAL THING

* *

Seven Self-Defense Methods
You Can Practice On Your
Barbie Doll

* * *

BITE SCRATCH AND KICK!
You're A Kid, And You're
Not Expected To Fight Fair!

ALWAYS CARRY EXTRA CANDY!
Every Bully Has His Price!

* * *

CONVINCING YOUR ASSAILANT
YOU'VE GOT A BIG BROTHER

* *

When All Else Fails . . . Cry!

Self-Defense For
HOUSEWIVES

HOW TO GIVE A GOOD KARATE CHOP TO A
BUTCHER WHO GAVE YOU A BAD PORK CHOP

Sex Appeal: *Your Most Valuable Weapon For
Avoiding A Traffic Ticket*

HOW TO AVOID A TRAFFIC TICKET...
AND A MORALS CHARGE

*Self Defense Against White Tornadoes, Giants In
Washers, Witches, Flying Maids, White Knights
and Gabby Lady Plumbers*

Self-Defense For ANIMAL LOVERS

HOW TO EAT A STEAK DINNER
SAFELY WHEN YOU OWN
THREE DOBERMAN PINSCHERS

• • •

4 Effective Judo Holds
You Can Use On A
Depraved Parakeet

• • •

BEING ATTACKED BY A
LAUGHING HYENA IS NOT
AS FUNNY AS IT SOUNDS

How To Deal With A Goldfish
Who's Been Watching Movies
About Barracudas On TV

• • •

PUTTING THE CAT OUT WHEN
HE DOESN'T WANT TO GO

How To Defend Yourself Against
Two—er—Six—er—Eighteen—er
—Seventy-Two-Crazed Rabbits

• • •

7 WAYS TO RELAX AND UNWIND
A NERVOUS BOA CONSTRICTOR

ARTIST: MORT DRUCKER   WRITER: LARRY SIEGEL

Hello! I'm sullen actor, **Warren Booty!** I recently starred in a great film epic about the Depression Era of the Thirties. I got the part because I'm a **sensitive** actor, I'm a **versatile** performer, and by a fantastic coincidence, I also happened to be the Producer!

This is my co-star, **Faye Runaway.** The historic couple we're supposed to play in this film were really ugly, savage killers. But after watching the movie for five minutes, you'll know at once what famous American couple we're really portraying . . . **Steve and Eydie Lawrence!**

This picture deals with one of the most violent crime waves in American history.

Oh, by the way, the girl who just walked in is my sister, Shirley MacKook! She recently starred in "Woman Times Eight"! But that was another violent crime . . .

BALMY AND CLOD

Some people have asked me how I happen to be qualified to produce films at my age. Well, actually I am a great student of the motion picture. In fact, I've seen every movie that Walt Disney ever made. I just love his adorable little animals. And now, speaking of adorable little animals, here is the story of . . . .

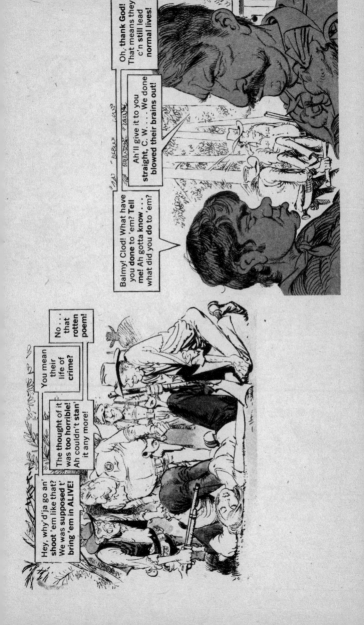

We're Young! We're Adorable! We Murder Millions!

WARREN BOOTY
FAYE RUNAWAY

as those beloved Nazi nuts...

History's most talked-about couple!

CO-STARRING
MICHAEL J. DULLARD as GOERING • GENE HACKHACK as GOEBBELS.
ESTELLE PARSNIPS as the irresistible ILSA KOCH

and featuring

EVA and DOLF

WRITTEN BY
DAVID NINNY and ROBERT BOOBY

DIRECTED BY
ARTHUR PINHEAD

PRODUCED BY
WARREN BOOTY

FROM AN IDEA
SUGGESTED BY THE CHASE MANHATTAN BANK

You Know You're
REALLY A

You Know You're REALLY A PARENT When . . .

. . . you suddenly find that your electric bill comes to three dollars less than you paid for batteries for toys that month!

You Know You're REALLY A PARENT When . . .

. . . the most dreaded event of the year is no longer "Income Tax" time, but that "Pre-Christmas Toy-Assembly" season!

ARTIST: PAUL COKER, JR.
WRITERS: PHIL HAHN
& JACK HANRAHAN

PARENT
When...

You Know You're REALLY A PARENT When . . .

. . . you whole-heartedly join an all-out campaign to wipe out those smutty books and magazines you used to read and enjoy!

You Know You're REALLY A PARENT When . . .

. . . you sit up all night preparing an off-the-cuff, informal explanation of the human reproductive process!

You Know You're REALLY A PARENT When . . .

. . . you find yourself carrying snapshots in your wallet where money used to be!

You Know You're REALLY A PARENT When . . .

. . . you insult the boss and his wife by leaving early rather than risk losing a good baby-sitter!

You Know You're REALLY A PARENT When . . .

. . . you pull the Road Atlas out of the glove compartment and find that its pages have been permanently fused together with Tootsie Rolls!

You Know You're REALLY A PARENT When . . .

. . . the conversation turns to doctors, and the only two names that come to mind are "Spock" and "Seuss"!

You Know You're REALLY A PARENT When . . .

. . . you're asked to solve some "New Math" problems, and it suddenly dawns on you that you never really understood the "Old Math"!

You Know You're REALLY A PARENT When . . .

. . . you catch yourself sneaking a bath with "Mr. Bubble"!

You Know You're REALLY A PARENT When . . .

. . . you never buy anything for the house
that isn't plastic, vinyl, or cast iron!

You Know You're REALLY A PARENT When . . .

. . . you discover that your alarm
clock has been broken for five years,
and you hadn't even noticed!

You Know You're REALLY A PARENT When . . .

. . . you discover you're brushing your teeth with "Pimple Cream"!

You Know You're REALLY A PARENT When . . .

. . . you run out of glasses and you have to start serving martinis in "Yogi Bear" mugs!

ALLEY-OOPS!

ARTIST & WRITER: SERGIO ARAGONES

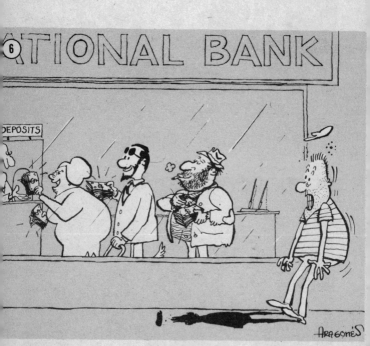

The life of a School Teacher is a monotonous one. And parents certainly aren't helping to relieve the dreariness with the hasty, uninformative, look-alike notes they write to explain the absence from class of Walter or Irving or Wendy or Lolita. The kids couldn't possibly have identical excuses any more than they could have identical home lives with identical mothers and fathers. But Teacher never gets a hint of their varied backgrounds from the parental scribblings they bring to school. MAD envisions the day when Mom and Dad may exert a little extra effort to write, in their own distinctive styles, some truly

PERSONAL-IZED

ABSENCE NOTES

WRITER: TOM KOCH

Merrill Lynch, Jr. was inactive yesterday due to unstable conditions which caused his temperature to hit an intra-day high of 102° and close at 101%, up 3 points from Wednesday's norm. This touched off a flurry of rumors that he might be planning to acquire the flu. However, such reports proved unsubstantiated this morning when he opened with 98%. Please excuse his absence, which can only be attributed to a speculative interest on the part of his short mother.

M. L. Piercefender

BATSTEEN, BARSTEEN, DURSTEEN & FLANG
ADVERTISING CONSULTANTS

2613 Madison Avenue
New York, N.Y. 10018

LQ 3-2000, Phone Numberwise
BATFLANG, Cable Addresswise

Please excuse Sumner's absence yesterday, classroomwise. He was at the Den-
tist, six-month check-upwise, having
his 28% fewer cavities filled after
brushing regularly with the new, im-
proved <u>CREST</u> containing the miracle in-
gredient <u>FLUORISTAN.</u>

With utmost sincerity,

Rubert C. Widgewood

Rubert C. Widgewood
Account Executive

Falvy
Animal Hospital
85 Pilchick Drive,
Kinosha, Wisc.

*Newton couldn't
come to school
last week because
he pulled a tendon
in his left hind
fetlock.*

*J. J. Falvy, D.V.M.
Doctor of Veterinary
Medicine*

TIME
THE WEEKLY NEWSMAGAZINE
Time-Life Building, New York City

The small, tow-headed moppet with the sad face entered the dining room of the comfortable frame house in fashionable, suburban White Plains one morning last week clad in the familiar orange and blue striped bathrobe his maternal grandmother had given him for his eighth birthday. It might have been just another school day for young Maynard Bindsturm. But the ghastly red blotches already beginning to erupt on his fevered forehead gave warning that this was destined to be no ordinary day. Maynard Bindsturm had come down with the measles.

Yours truly,

Llewelyn Bindsturm

Llewelyn Bindsturm

Now hear this!

1. You are hereby commanded to grant full amnesty to Nimitz Halsey Earnshaw (a civilian minor) re: absence without leave 24 February 1967 between the hours of 0830 and 1500.

2. He had an upset stomach.

Warren V. Earnshaw

Warren V. Earnshaw,
Rear Admiral, U.S.N. (Ret.)

FENWICK L. FROYD, M.D.

Consulting Psychiatrist,
1460 Libido Drive, Tenafly, New Jersey

> Fenwick, Jr., spent the day at home
> in a closet, yesterday, suffering
> from a deep emotional disturbance
> brought on by receiving a "D-minus"
> in Social Studies. I hope that you
> are sufficiently mature enough to
> beg him to excuse you for your
> display of hostility and rejection.

MELLOW LEAF TOBACCO CO.
Boondock, North Carolina

To Whom It May Concern:

Arnold was out of school yesterday with a cold, but I am letting
him return today against doctor's orders because there is no
conclusive medical proof that
sneezing ever transmitted a cold
to anyone. However, for my own
legal protection, please post
the following notice on your bul-
letin board:

CAUTION: LETTING ARNOLD
BREATHE ON YOU MAY BE
HAZARDOUS TO YOUR HEALTH!

Sincerely,

Beauregard Lee Flaunk

Beauregard Lee Flaunk,
President

LOUIS G. GROWST

CERTIFIED PUBLIC ACCOUNTANT
325 BROADWAY, PHILADELPHIA, PA.

The youngest of my three daughters, Maudie, was not present for the first 0.7% of the current fiscal semester due to congestion in 38% of her bronchial tubes, necessitating deductible expenditures of $17.25 for medical treatment and drugs.

Louis G. Growst, C.P.A.

HUMNER & OVERDRIFT

Funeral Directors, Maudlin, Mo.
"Sharing Your Grief Since 1906"

Allow me to express my deepest sorrow over the tragic and untimely departure of Sylvia from your midst yesterday. I feel certain that she was sadly missed by the host of friends and classmates she left behind. But she had to run out of the room fast and hurry home to throw up.

Mournfully, L.V. Humner

Why in heck is it called "Sandlot Baseball"? *We* usually played it in a weedy field —or a muddy tract—or a paved schoolyard! One thing's for certain, we *never* played on *sand!* In fact, the young people's whole approach to America's national pastime was very different back then. We'll show you what we mean as MAD takes

A Nostalgic Look At

SANDLOT BASEBALL

ARTIST: PAUL COKER, JR.   WRITER: DEAN NORMAN

Before any game, we had to mark out the "Diamond" . . .

Next, we had to choose up sides—and then you really found out how you rated with your buddies!

Aw, we don't want him! You can have him!

Okay! If we gotta take him, you gotta give us a good guy, too!

Why don't we let him pitch for both sides? That would be even!?

Yeah, but whoever bats second would never get to bat!

It was settled by letting the team that had to take you be the first side to bat. Then the other team took the field and spent the next half hour arguing over who would play what position . . .

Somebody's got to play right field! We can't ALL play left field!

Why not? Nobody ever hits to right field anyway!

I'm pitcher 'cause it's my ball!

I got first base!

I said "I got first!" first!

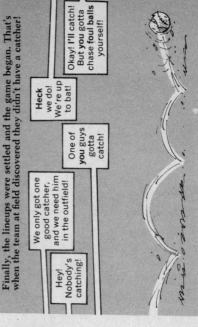

Finally, the lineups were settled and the game began. That's when the team at field discovered they didn't have a catcher!

. . . meanwhile, your side was fighting over the batting order!

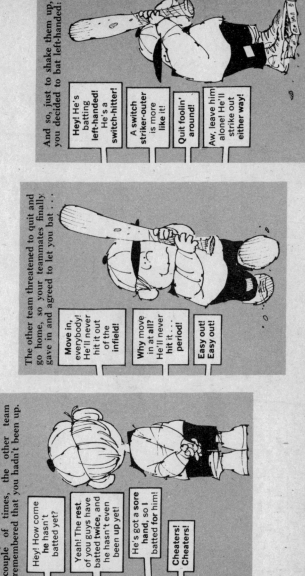

Then you ran to third base and started a rhubarb . . .

While the other side was trying to find the ball in the bushes, you ran to second base.

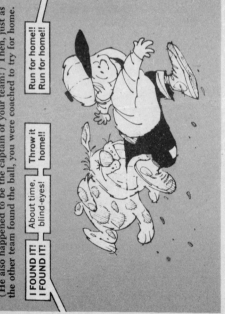

Finally, after your team had batted around three more times (and you struck out each time—twice left-handed and once right-handed), it was your turn to take the field. Your team decided that right field was the safest place to put you . . .

Nobody ever hits it to right field!

Go way out!

Yeah! Way, way, way out!

Even though nobody could hear you way out there in right field, you kept up a lively round of chatter.

Atta boy! Atta boy!

Put it in there!

Three up! Three down!

Easy out! Easy out!

Let's go, gang! Let's go!

The other team batted around, and after a while your mind sort of wandered. Then, all of a sudden, you heard your teammates shouting at you. The best batter on the other team had crossed them up by batting left-handed, and he'd hit a long fly ball to right field!

WAKE UP OUT THERE!

CATCH IT! CATCH IT!

At first, you thought the ball was going way back over your head, and so you ran out . . .

CATCH IT! CATCH IT!

He'll never catch it!

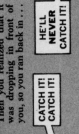

Then you realized that it was dropping in front of you, so you ran back in . . .

CATCH IT! CATCH IT!

HE'LL NEVER CATCH IT!

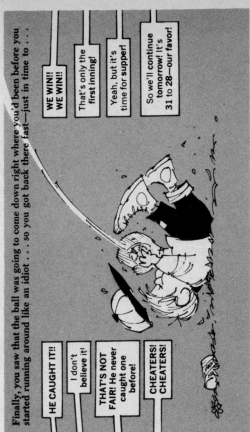

Finally, you saw that the ball was going to come down right where you'd been before you started running around like an idiot . . . so you got back there fast—just in time to . . .

HE CAUGHT IT!!

I don't believe it!

THAT'S NOT FAIR! He never caught one before!

CHEATERS! CHEATERS!

WE WIN!! WE WIN!!

That's only the first inning!

Yeah, but it's time for supper!

So we'll continue tomorrow! It's 31 to 28—our favor!

Well, that's how "Sandlot Baseball" was. If you were a kid today, it would be a lot different. You'd play in a "Little League" and wear a real uniform and use real equipment like balls with covers and bases for bases. And you wouldn't waste a lot of time standing around and arguing, because grown-ups would be organizing and supervising your games. But there's one thing you might not like about it, though. You still wouldn't get to play . . . . because you'd still be the worst player in the neighborhood!

Put it in there!

Easy out! Easy out!

Three up! Three down!

Atta boy! Atta boy!

Let's go, gang! Let's go!

And so, even though you were the star of the game, you were modest about it . . . until you got home!

HEY, DAD! I HIT A HOMERUN . . . AND I CAUGHT BILLY'S LONG FLY . . . AND I WON THE GAME FOR OUR SIDE!

Nice going, Son! Maybe you'll be a Big League Ballplayer someday after all!

WHILE

STROLLING

THROUGH

THE CITY

Have you ever made a bragging remark or a hostile statement or an antagonizing pronouncement, only to have it explode in your face? Then perhaps you'll identify with a few of the idiots in the following situations who were prompted to say

"ME AND MY BIG MOUTH!"

ARTIST: AL JAFFEE

WRITER: DEAN NORMAN

I don't care if it's only some little **10-cent trinket**! It's the **thought** that counts!

Man, if they **want** me, they'll have to come and get me!

THE
LIGHTER
SIDE
OF
DRIVING

WRITER & ARTIST : DAVID BERG

Isn't that **festive!** Every year, they really **out-do** themselves during the holiday season, decorating the streets with blinking red, yellow and green lights—and plastic snowflakes—and jolly Santas—and wreaths! I tell you, it's **absolutely gorgeous!**

All right! **I know** it's beautiful! But **how long** are you going to just **sit here** and look at the **lights?**

Until I can figure out **which** one of those gorgeous lights is the **TRAFFIC LIGHT!!**

For hundreds of years, folk singers have been composing ditties to voice their criticism of the way the world is being run. But not until recently did protest songs suddenly zoom to the top on music popularity charts. Unfortunately, the phenomenon may not last long. This generation's angry young protest singers are beginning to show a definite need for new material. And so it is that MAD rushes forward to keep a good thing going (or kill it off completely) by presenting this inspired array of . . .

New "Protests" To The Same Old Tunes

ARTIST: BOB CLARKE
WRITER: TOM KOCH

A Rousing Sneer

For The Undedicated Physician

(Sung to the tune of "*Home on the Range*")

Groan, groan with the pain.
Your doctor has vanished again.
Of course, it's his right
To go out Friday night,
So just lie there. Shut up! Don't complain!

Writhe, twitch and feel strange.
You've left word with Doc's phone exchange.
Some day, he'll check in
And prescribe as-pir-in.
That's the best you can hope to arrange.

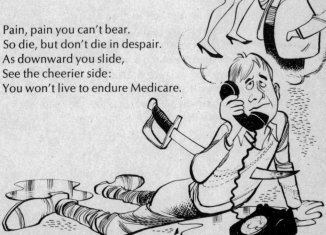

Retch, whimper and bawl,
As down to Doc's office you crawl.
It's painfully slow,
But that's where you must go
'Cause you know he won't
      make a house call.

Pain, pain you can't bear.
So die, but don't die in despair.
As downward you slide,
See the cheerier side:
You won't live to endure Medicare.

The TV Victim's Lament

(Sung to the tune of "Blowin' in the Wind")

How many times must a guy spray with Ban
      Before he doesn't offend?
And how many times must he gargle each day
      Before he can talk to a friend?
How many tubes of shampoo must he buy
      Before his dandruff will end?
The sponsors, my friend, will sell you all they can.
      The sponsors will sell you all they can.

How many times must a man use Gillette
      Before shaving won't make him bleed?
And how many cartons of Kents must he smoke
      Before the girls all pay him heed?
How many products must one person buy
      Before he has all that he'll need?
The sponsors, my friend, will sell you all they can.
      The sponsors will sell you all they can.

How many times must a gal clean her sink
      Before Ajax scours that stain,
And how many times must she rub in Ben-Gay
      Before she can rub out the pain?
How many ads on TV must we watch
      Before we are driven insane?
The sponsors, my friend, will broadcast all they can.
      The sponsors will broadcast all they can!

The Smog Breathers' Final Gasp

(Sung to the tune of "*The Midnight Special*")

See the steel mill furnace
Belch its smoke at me,
While I inhale deeply
'Til I'm ready for lung surgery.

Now, you wake up in the morning, and you strangle like mad.
Poison's blowing in the window, and you're feeling kind of bad.
Tongue's all coated gold with sulphur; both your eyes are bright
You're a lovely blend of colors, but before long you'll be dead.

Still, the steel mill smokestack
Blows its crud at me,
Causing awful headaches
Plus assorted other misery.

City Hall is swamped with letters. "Clean the air," they all·say.
But the mayor's secretary quickly files them all away.
No dough's left to fight pollution, so don't bother·to grouse;
It all went to air condition every politician's house.

So just let that smokestack
Belch its fumes at me.
Since it's good for business,
I'll lie down and conk out quietly.

Peeved At Obstructions

(Sung to the tune of "Eve of Destruction")

You save up all year long to take a nice vacation.
You make a lot of plans to drive across the nation.
You dream of all you'll see with great anticipation.
You've only got a week to reach your destination,
But that seems like enough; you feel no consternation.
Then they tell you over and over and over again, my friend,
That you can't get through; the road is under construction.

You've never been to Maine or Utah's scenic section.
You call the auto club to help make your selection.
You pay to get your car a thorough trip inspection
So you can drive afar and feel you've got protection.
Then, when you're almost there, you seek a cop's direction.
And he tells you over and over and over again, my friend,
That you must turn back; the road is under construction.

Vacation here at home, our president keeps saying.
Don't spend your dough abroad, he fervently is praying.
So you head for New York to do your summer playing;
Or maybe to the west a travel plan you're laying,
To see those snowy peaks and geysers wildly spraying.
But the signs warn over and over and over again, my friend,
That you can't get there; the road is under construction.

The Flower Children's Fight Song

(Sung to the tune of *"They Call the Wind Maria"*)

The squares can't bear to see us wear
Our clothes unwashed and baggy.
They say it's wrong to have hair long,
And they call us downright shaggy.
We're shaggy.
We're shaggy.
They hate us 'cause we're shaggy.

We've got a right to look a fright,
And smell this strong or stronger.
We won't be sheared of locks or beard,
But we may let both grow longer.
And shaggy;
And shaggy.
Down to our knees and shaggy!

We won't conform to any norm.
We'll keep our sweat shirts raggy,
'Til those who fuss approve of us.
Then there's no point staying shaggy.
Unshaggy.
Unshaggy.
We'll bathe and be unshaggy.

The Roving Postman

(Sung to the tune of *"The Roving Gambler"*)

I am a roving postman.
I walk from street to street,
With so much junk mail in the pouch I tote
It's flattened both my feet.

I used to just bring letters,
And folks were fond of me.
Now, they know me best for the trash I dump;
I'm yelled at constantly.

It's surely not my fault, though;
I can't control the mails.
And I get no kicks passing out bright ads
Announcing casket sales.

I'm lugging sixty pounds here
Of junk no one could want;
Mostly sample jars of some mustache wax
Addressed to "Occupant."

But still I trod my route, boys,
Through snow and sleet and hail.
Then I hurry home when the day is done
And burn my own junk mail.

The Bleat Of The Former Pedestrian

(Sung to the tune of "Kisses Sweeter than Wine")

When I was a young man without any car,
I used to hang around home and not go very far.
I had me no wheels and no gas in the tank.
In fact, I really had nothing but dough in the bank.
O-o-h-h-h, oh, money that was all mine.

Then I met a dealer and showed him my cash.
He said, "My boy, what you need is this '52 Nash."
The contract I signed was to drive me to tears;
It called for low, easy terms for the next hundred years.
O-o-h-h-h, oh, money no longer mine.

I don't like to protest; I'm just not that kind,
But then my grounds for complaint are so easy to find.
The license and tax are outrageously high,
And when you go to insure, kiss your savings good-bye.
O-o-h-h-h, oh, money used to be mine.

I've heard it proclaimed, though I'm not really sure,
That there's a federal program to help out the poor.
I don't ask for food or the Job Training Corps;
Just cash to finance my car for a dozen years more.
O-o-h-h-h, oh, money rightfully mine.

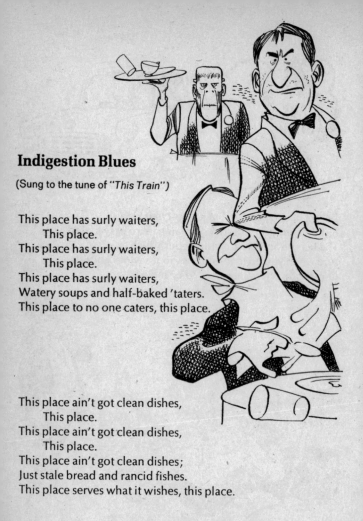

Indigestion Blues

(Sung to the tune of *"This Train"*)

This place has surly waiters,
    This place.
This place has surly waiters,
    This place.
This place has surly waiters,
Watery soups and half-baked 'taters.
This place to no one caters, this place.

This place ain't got clean dishes,
    This place.
This place ain't got clean dishes,
    This place.
This place ain't got clean dishes;
Just stale bread and rancid fishes.
This place serves what it wishes, this place.

This place has two main courses,
    This place.
This place has two main courses,
    This place.
This place has two main courses—
Both are drenched with thick brown sauces
Camouflaging meat from horses, this place.

Concerto In D-Minus

(Sung to the tune of *"Tom Dooley"*)

Lift up your head and study!
Learn or you're doomed to fail!
And if your mind stays muddy,
You'll never go to Yale.

No college really wants you;
Not Georgia or Bucknell.
Why should they come and hunt you?
You don't play football well.

Lift up your head and read, boy!
Stay up all night and cram!
If you lack grades you need, boy,
You'll go to Uncle Sam.

I'm Cross About Inflation

(Sung to the tune of "*Across the Wide Missouri*")

The lunch at school's a dollar-twenty.
Go away, you wild inflation.
For creamed chipped beef, four-bits is plenty.
Go way. I cannot pay to keep up with inflation

Three bucks I saved by being thrifty;
Money for a date this week-end.
But movies charge at least two-fifty.
And so, I'll see the show all by myself this week-end.

I mowed the lawn and earned two-dollars:
Lowest wage scale in the nation.
But ask for more and my dad hollers:
"It's you. It's kids like you who cause the wild inflation."

Several issues back, we ran an article entitled "The MAD Hate Book", in which we demonstrated to readers how to feel better by blowing off steam about pet hates. The response was more than gratifying. An avalanche of letters poured in from readers blowing off steam about their pet hates—mainly "MAD" and "The MAD Hate Book" article. And so, not to be out-done in the hostility department, here we go again with another more aggravating and exacerbating chapter of . . .

THE MAD HATE BOOK VOL. II

ARTIST & WRITER:
AL JAFFEE

Don't you hate... being unanimously chosen for a repulsive role in your school play!

Don't you hate... when you tell people to "drop
in any time!"... and they do!

Don't you hate... dripping window
air-conditioners!

Don't you hate... discovering there are no towels
after you've just taken a bath!

Don't you hate... meeting a luscious, sexy doll
at a big "Family Affair", and
discovering she's a first cousin!

Don't you hate... when something ecch-y
suddenly comes out of the
wrong end of the tube!

Don't you hate... imbeciles who honk their horns the
split second after the light turns green!

Don't you hate... finding out that the person you were
tearing apart all through dinner was
in the next booth all the time!

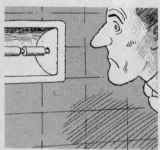

Don't you hate... being surprised
by an empty
tissue dispenser!

Don't you hate... finding that bar of chocolate you
stuck into your pocket "for only
a moment" eight hours later!

Don't you hate... gas station attendants who insist on "rounding out" the amount of your purchase so you end up paying for gas that overflowed onto the ground!

Don't you hate... people who never properly replace screw-tops on jars!

Don't you hate... lunch counter-tops with colorful patterns that completely camouflage spilled foods and sauces!

Don't you hate . . . parking lot attendants who zoom off
in your new car like it was a 727 jet!

Don't you hate . . . never knowing what your doctor or
your lawyer's fee will eventually be!

Don't you hate . . . proud parents who insist on letting
you enjoy the ecstatic pleasure of
holding their brand new baby!

Don't you hate ... neighbors who barbecue steaks when
you're downwind serving tuna fish!

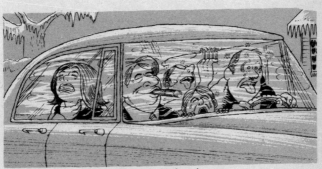

Don't you hate ... birdbrains who smoke cigars in a car
when it's too cold to open a window!

Don't you hate ... yourself for tipping
when you know darn well
the service was terrible!

Don't you hate... meeting a school representative when you're supposed to be home ... sick!

Don't you hate... hearing a crunching sound while looking for a lost contact lens!

Don't you hate... civil servants who know they can't lose their jobs no matter how uncivilly they treat you

Don't you hate... big guys who smoke in "No Smoking" areas!

Don't you hate... store clerks who can't answer a single question without first checking with the Manager!

Don't you hate... borrowing a car, and suddenly discovering it has power brakes!

Don't you hate . . . when something goes "On Sale" the day after you bought it!

Don't you hate . . . people who ask questions and pay no attention to the answers!

Don't you hate . . . a date who describes the qualities her "ideal man" should have, and none of them fit you!

Don't you hate... vending machines that tell you to write for your money back if they don't work, and the postage costs more than you lost!

Don't you hate... finding out you have no handkerchief right after a viscous sneeze!

Don't you hate... magazines that print sequels to articles that never should have been run in the first place!

THE LIGHTER

SIDE OF
HOBBIES

WRITER & ARTIST: DAVID BERG

Hey! Where's everybody going?

Finished!

FINISHED!?? We started making the same model at the **same time** and I'm only **half** done! How can you **possibly** be finished so fast?

It's **very simple!** I am **extremely dexterous,** I work **systematically and rapidly**—my **mind** racing ahead to the **next step,** I have **mastered** the technique of applying **just the right amount of cement . . .**

. . . and I leave out a great many parts!

Y'know, we **boys** are always involved in some **hobby** or other, like **collecting gum cards**, or **flying kites**, or **building models**, or foolin' around with **chemistry sets**!

Yeah—we boys play **baseball** and **football** and **basketball**! Those are like hobbies, **too**!

But the **girls**!! They're not **like** us boys! They don't do **nothing**!

Yeah! Take my **big sister**, f'rinstance! All she does is put her **hair** up, and put on **eye make-up**, and buy **clothes**, and talk on the **phone**!

I HEARD THAT!! You boys think you're so **great**? Well, it just so happens we girls **HAVE a hobby!!**

Oh, yeah! What **is** it?

BOYS!!

Hey, there's **Al Jaffee!** He's a **professional artist!** He went to some of the **best art schools** in the country! I'd **love** to ask him what he thinks of my work!

So!? Let's call him in and **ask** him!

I'll bet he tells me I'm an **undiscovered genius**—an amateur with **tremendous talent!**

Well, it's **not bad** for a **beginner!** But you've got to learn to **crawl** before you can **walk!** First, you'll have to learn the **"basics"**—like **perspective** . . . and **anatomy** . . . and **composition!** It takes years of **study** and **hard work** before one can attain a measure of proficiency in Art . . .

Ahhh . . . what does he know !

My husband is one of those **hobby nuts!** He goes from hobby to hobby—each time with the **same fantastic enthusiasm.** First there was **Stamps,** then **Ham Radio,** then **First Editions!**

Well, you know what his **real** hobby is? **Boring the heck out of me!** All he does is talk, talk, talk about his **stupid hobby!** Why, his **latest** hobby has driven me **so** wild, I've taken up a **little hobby of my own!**

Since I know I can **confide** in you, I'll tell you about **MY hobby!** He's **six feet tall** with **wavy hair,** and he doesn't **bore** me to death with **hobby talk!** So **I'm happy**—and what my **husband** doesn't know won't hurt **me!**

By the way, what **IS** your husband's latest hobby?

He's got a tape recorder!

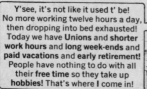

ON THE ROAD

with

Sergio Aragones

BECAUSE IT'S AROUND THE TIME OF YEAR WHEN INTEREST IN THIS SORT OF MUCK IS AT ITS HEIGHT, MAD NOW PROUDLY PRESENTS A COLLECTION OF . . .

Mother's Day Cards

Down Through History

ARTIST: BOB CLARKE   WRITER: FRANK JACOBS

From Abel

TO MOTHER —
ON MOTHERS DAY IT MUST BE FUN
TO BE THE FIRST AND ONLY ONE;
IN FACT, WITH PA YOU'VE SET THE PACE
FOR ALL THE FUTURE HUMAN RACE;
YOU'VE RAISED ME LIKE A MOTHER SHOULD
TO BE RESPECTFUL, FINE AND GOOD;
BUT, MA, TO PUT IT VERY PLAIN —
IT <u>KILLS</u> ME HOW YOU'RE RAISING CAIN!
— ABEL

From Cotton Mather

To Mother

When I was just a little lad,
    You filled my heart with fears;
You'd tell me how the world was bad,
    And then you'd box my ears;
You taught me that to wipe out sin
    All witches should be burned;
Tomorrow, when we drag you in,
    I'll show you what I've learned!

From Captain Kidd

Yo-Ho-Happy Mother's Day!

Oh, Mother dear, I speak your name
*   With every prize I plunder;*
I see your face within the flame
*   Of ships I tear asunder;*
I let no man stand in my way—
*   I strike and scourge and smother;*
For everything I am today,
*   I learned from you, dear Mother!*

From P. T. Barnum

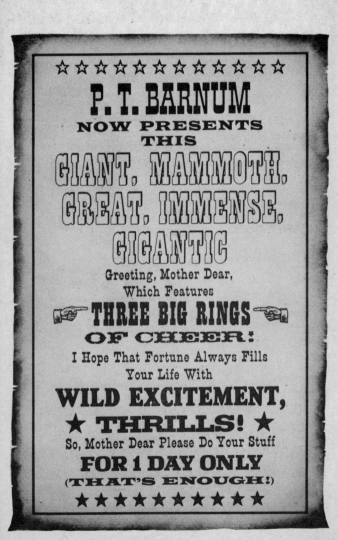

From Noah Webster

What Mother's Day Means To Me:

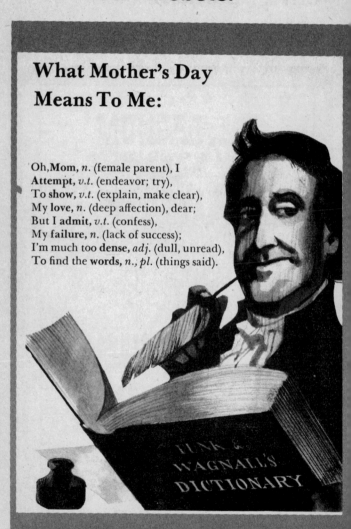

Oh, **Mom,** *n.* (female parent), I
Attempt, *v.t.* (endeavor; try),
To **show,** *v.t.* (explain, make clear),
My **love,** *n.* (deep affection), dear;
But I **admit,** *v.t.* (confess),
My **failure,** *n.* (lack of success);
I'm much too **dense,** *adj.* (dull, unread),
To find the **words,** *n., pl.* (things said).

FUNK &
WAGNALL'S
DICTIONARY

TO MOTHER

This day of yours I shall defend
    With all that's in my power;
No Iron Curtain shall descend
    To mar your Finest Hour;
And if the British nation should
    Last for a thousand years—
They'll know that if your day's not good,
    I'll shed Blood, Sweat and Tears!

From Ludwig van Beethoven

A Mother's Day Sonata

To you, dear Mother, I devote
This tender, sweet, adoring ♩ ;
To you, who loved to nag and carp,
Whose screaming voice was shrill and ♯ ;
To you who shrieked I was a brat
And locked me in our humble ♭ ;
No wonder, Mom, I found it best
To leave you just to get some 𝄾 !

From James McNeill Whistler

Oh, Mother dear, so sweet and kind,
    It's you I'm thinking of;
I wish that I could only find
    A way to prove my love;
How sad that others can't be shown
    The beauty that I see;
Alas! You'll always be unknown
    To everyone but me!

A Mother's Day Remembrance

From Sigmund Freud

Some Conscious (And Unconscious) Thoughts On Mother's Day

Oh, Mother dear, our love is true;
  (What causes this obsession?)
Sweet sentiments I send to you;
  (How come this deep depression?)
My heart for you is filled with joy;
  (What hostile thoughts I think now!)
You are my girl; I am your boy.
  (I'd better see my Shrink now!)

From Henry Ford

TO A MODEL-A MOTHER

I'm speeding off this note to you,
Oh, Mother dear, so good and true;
I hope you're rolling in high gear
As down the road of life you steer;
I'll choke and throttle anyone
Who horns in on your day of fun;
And should you drive yourself too much,
I'll always be there in the clutch!

See Dick.
See Jane.
See Dick and Jane.
See Jane run.
See Dick run.
See Dick run after Jane.
Run, Dick, run.
But be careful.
Because if Jane is caught
You might find yourself reading...

THE MAD
Getting
Married
PRIMER

Illustrated By
Jack Rickard

Written By
Dick De Bartolo

Lesson 1.
The Engagement Ring

See the diamond engagement ring.
See how it sparkles.
Sparkle, sparkle, sparkle.
See how the Bride-to-be shows it off.
She shows it to her friends
(To get them jealous).
She shows it to her relatives
(To get their admiration).
She shows it to her jeweler
(To get his appraisal).
Accepting a diamond engagement ring
Usually depends upon the approval of all three.
A diamond ring symbolizes a permanent commitment
Between the Groom-to-be and the Bride-to-be.
A diamond ring also symbolizes a permanent commitment
Between the Groom-to-be and the Finance Company.

Lesson 2.
The Wedding Invitations

See the Wedding Invitations.
They are black and white.
And cost much green.
Some clearly say:
"We request your presence at the Church . . ."
Others clearly say:
"We request your presence at the Reception . . ."
They all clearly imply:
"We request your presents . . ."
Presents, presents, presents.

Lesson 3.
The Bachelor Party

Just before the Wedding,
The Groom-to-be's male friends
Usually throw him a Bachelor Party . . .
At which they usually show a "Special Film".
Hoot, hollar, whistle.
See this particular Bachelor Party.
Hear everybody hoot and hollar and whistle.
Everybody is having a wonderful time—
Except the Groom-to-be.
He has just realized
The girl in the "Special Film"
Is his Bride-to-be.

Lesson 4.
The Bridal Shower

Just before the Wedding,
The Bride-to-be's female friends
Usually throw her a Bridal Shower . . .
At which they usually give her "Useful Items".
Like irons, and hair-dryers, and broilers.
Why are these items "useful". . .
When the new Bride will be sending her laundry out,
And going to a beauty parlor,
And eating in restaurants every night?
These items will be useful as *gifts*
At *future* Bridal Showers.

Lesson 5.
The Well-Wishers

See the Bride come down the aisle.
See the Groom come down the aisle.
See the people crying.
Sob, sob, sob.
The Bride's family and friends are crying:
"Such a beautiful girl . . .
Marrying such an ugly clod!"
The Groom's family and friends are crying:
"Such a handsome man . . .
Marrying such an ugly witch!"
Some people are so unhappy at weddings.
Then there are people who are *extremely* happy at weddings:
The Caterer, the Minister, the Florist, the Printer, the Jeweler,
The Dressmaker, the Orchestra, the Photographer, etc. etc.

Lesson 6.

The Wedding Ceremony

See the Minister conducting the Wedding Ceremony.
He says:
"Do you take this man to be your lawfully wedded husband?"
The Bride answers:
"I do."
He asks:
"Do you take this woman to be your lawfully wedded wife?"
The Groom answers:
"I do."
This is the last time the Bride and Groom will
    agree on anything.
The Minister asks if there are any reasons
Why these two should not be joined in Holy Matrimony.
Too bad the question isn't asked a *year* from now.
There'll be *plenty* of reasons.

Lesson 7.
The Best Man

See the Best Man.
He and the Groom were best friends.
They bowled together, and golfed together,
And drank together, and played cards together.
Today is the last time they will ever see each other.
But there will still be bowling, and golfing,
And drinking, and playing cards.
Except that the Groom will be working
While the Bride will be doing them.

Lesson 8.
The Bouquet

See the Bride throw her Bouquet.
See all the Bridesmaids run.
Run, run, run.
See the woman in front catch the Bouquet.
She couldn't get out of the way in time.
According to tradition, the *next* one to marry
Will be the Bride's High School Teacher:
Sister Maria Theresa.

Lesson 9.
The Wedding Reception

See the Wedding Reception.
Everyone is dancing and drinking and eating like crazy.
You have to dance and drink and eat an awful lot
To cover the cost of a $50.00 wedding gift.
See the Bride eating a piece of Wedding Cake.
This is her 17th piece.
She has finally gained a husband.
And lost a diet.

Lesson 10.
The Getaway

See the Wedding Couple dancing with friends
And laughing with relatives,
And having a wonderful time at the Reception.
In the old days, the Bride and Groom
Would be anxious to make their Getaway,
So they could rush to a Honeymoon Retreat.
Rush, rush, rush.
Nowadays, the Bride and Groom
Are usually the last to leave the Reception.
They're not *that* anxious to rush to a Honeymoon Retreat
When they've been living together for the past two years.
Blush, blush, blush.

ONE DAY IN THE JUNGLE

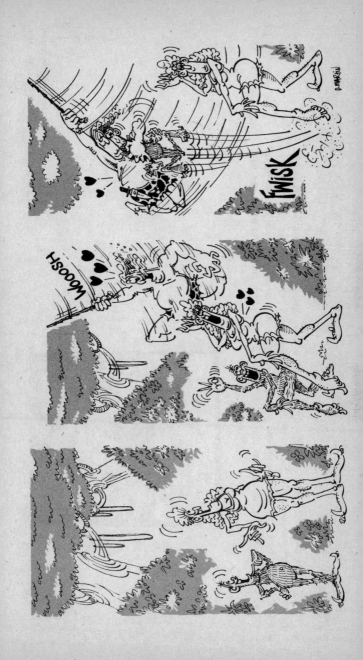

ESCAPE-GOAT DEPT.

Years ago, when they made a prison picture, you knew exactly what was going on. The guards were all sadistic and the prisoners were all regular guys under their tough exteriors. But today, things are different. Today, a prison picture isn't really about prison and prisoners. Today, it's all symbolism, and you have to figure out what's going on. Like f'rinstance in this MAD version of a recent prison picture that begins like this:

I get green gum balls! I get purple gum balls! I get white gum balls! But never ... never once in my whole life have I ever gotten a marbleized gum ball! So I'm smashin' every gum ball machine in this town until I get a marbleized gum ball!!

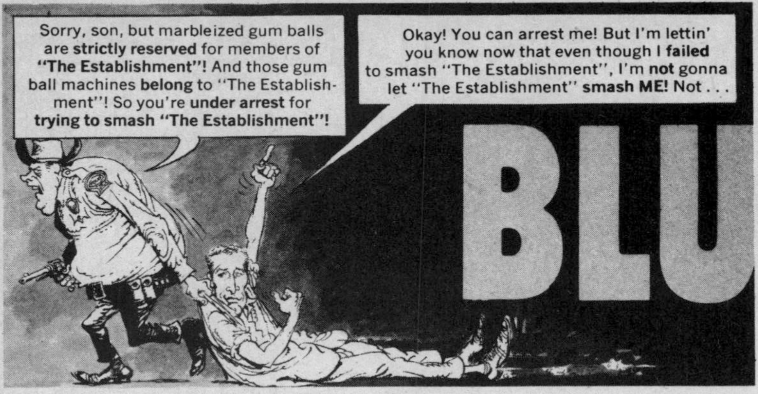

BLUE-EYED KOOK